Book 1

IN THE SHOP
Use your stickers to give these cars their missing parts.

WORLD TOUR

Place your stickers over the shadows to identify these characters.

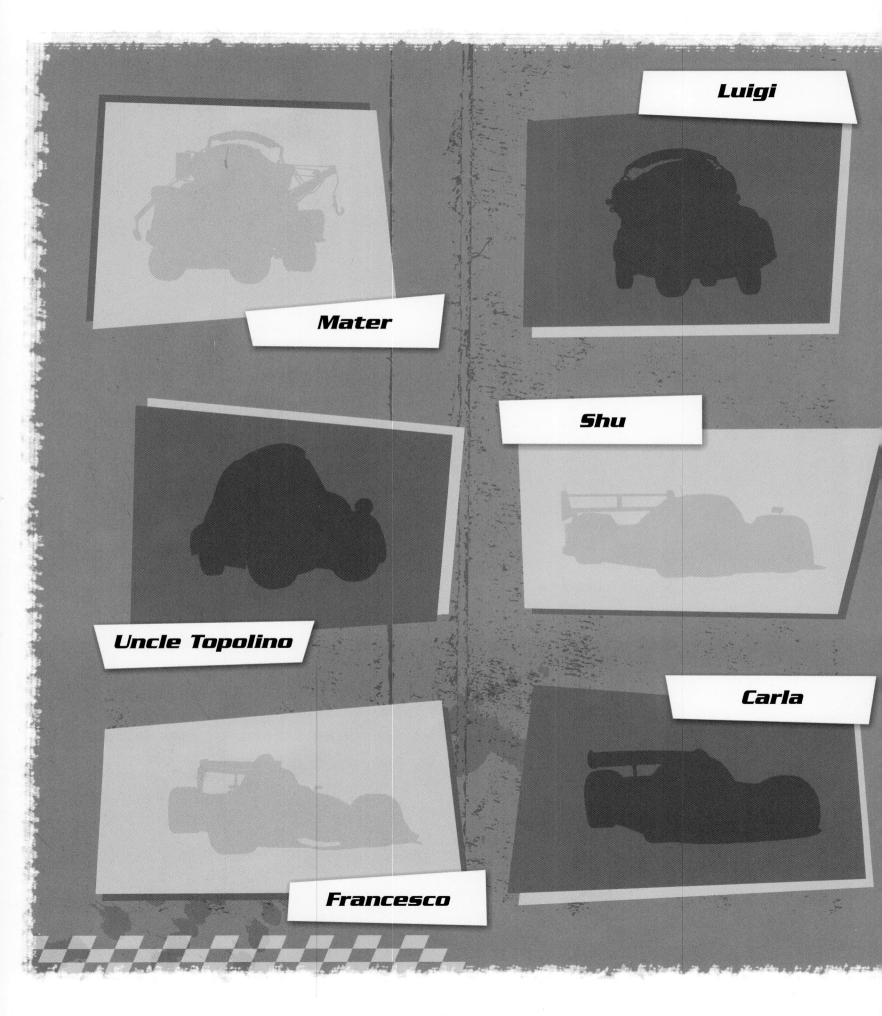

Luigi

Mater

Shu

Uncle Topolino

Carla

Francesco

Holley

Lightning

Professor Z

Tomber

Finn

Grem

CARS UP CLOSE

Use the close-ups as clues to discover the identities of these cars.

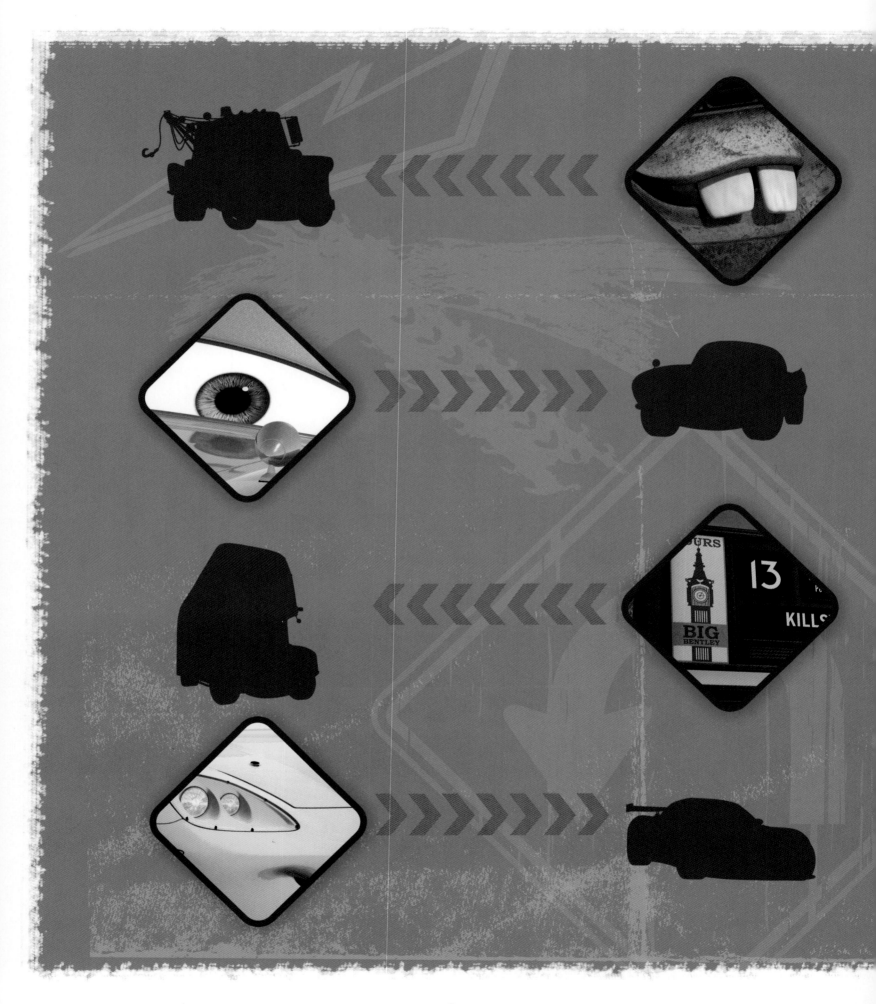

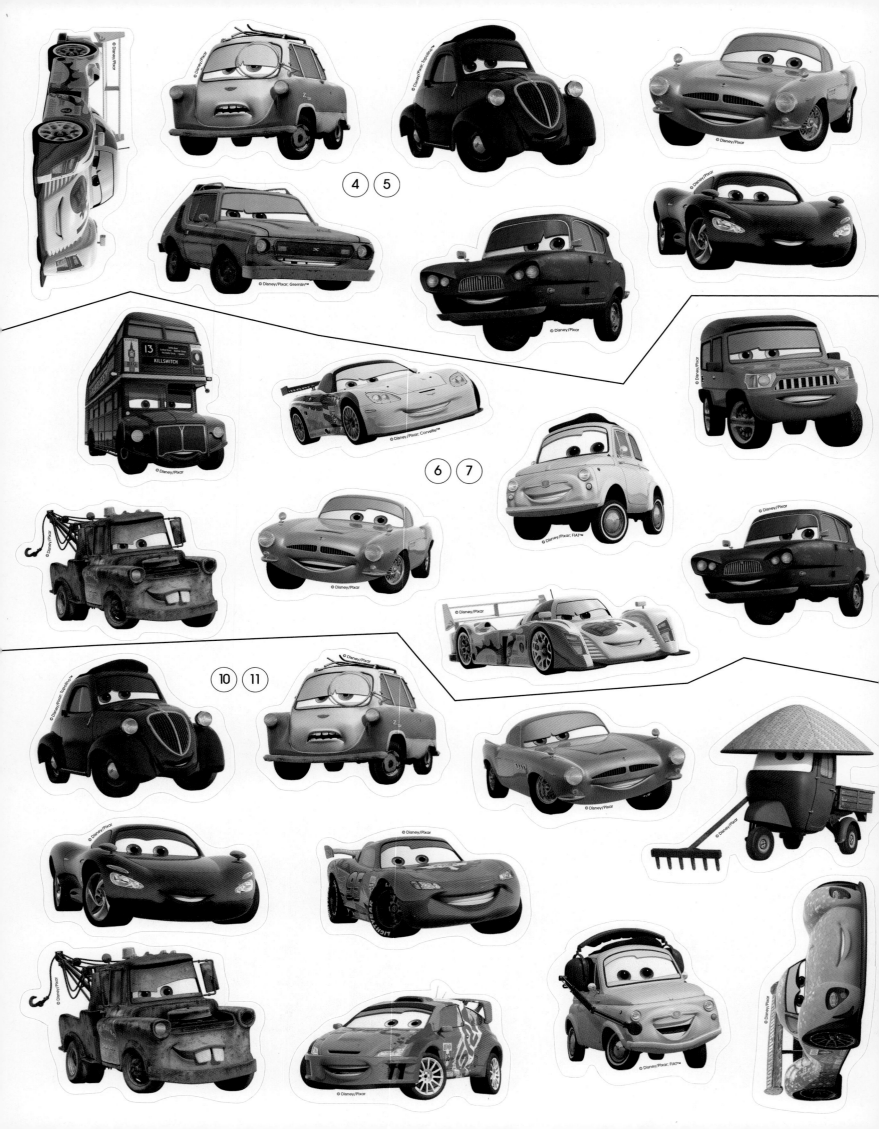

THE LINE-UP

Complete the vehicle patterns below with your stickers.

THE GOOD AND THE BAD
Use your stickers to identify the good guys and the villains.

Good Guys

Villains

CARS AROUND THE WORLD

Use your stickers to match the cars to the flags representing their home countries.

MEET YOU AT THE FINISH LINE!

Make the bottom scene look like the top one with your stickers.

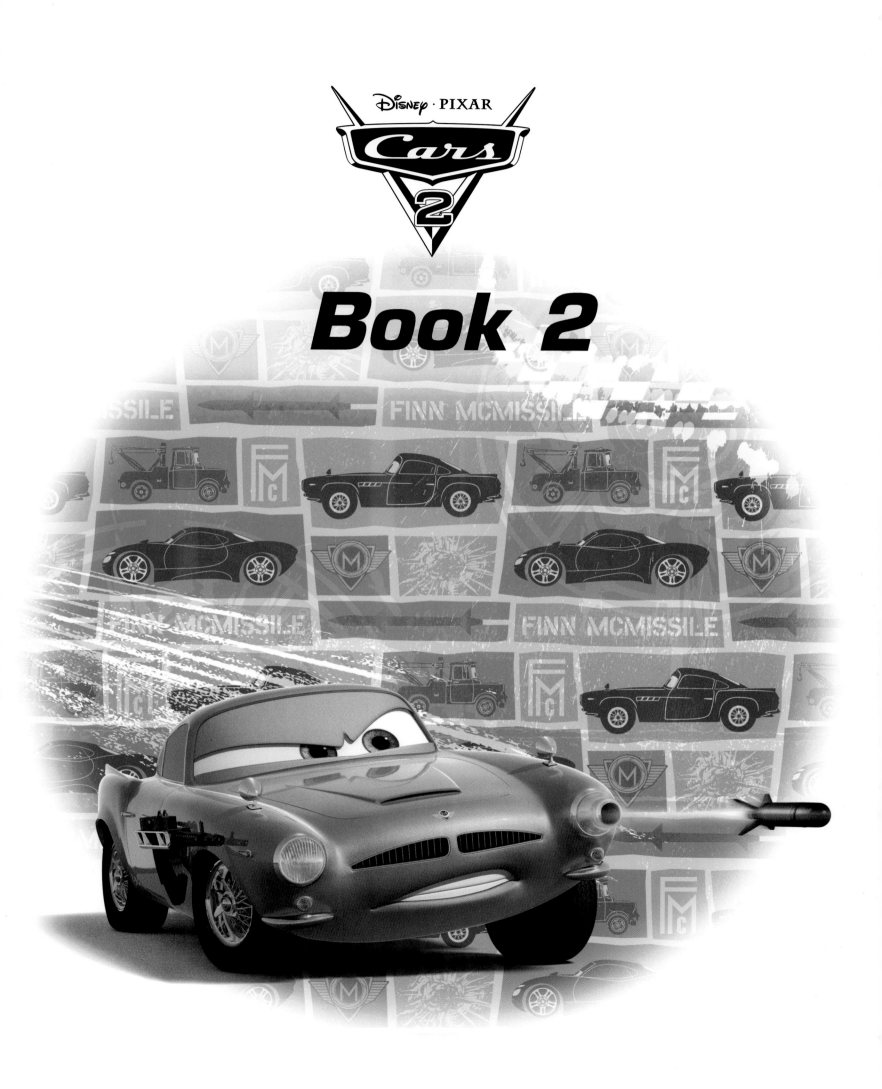

RACING COLOURS

Use your stickers to match each car to the right paint colours.

TEAMING UP
Some cars share things in common. Place your stickers over the correct shadows.

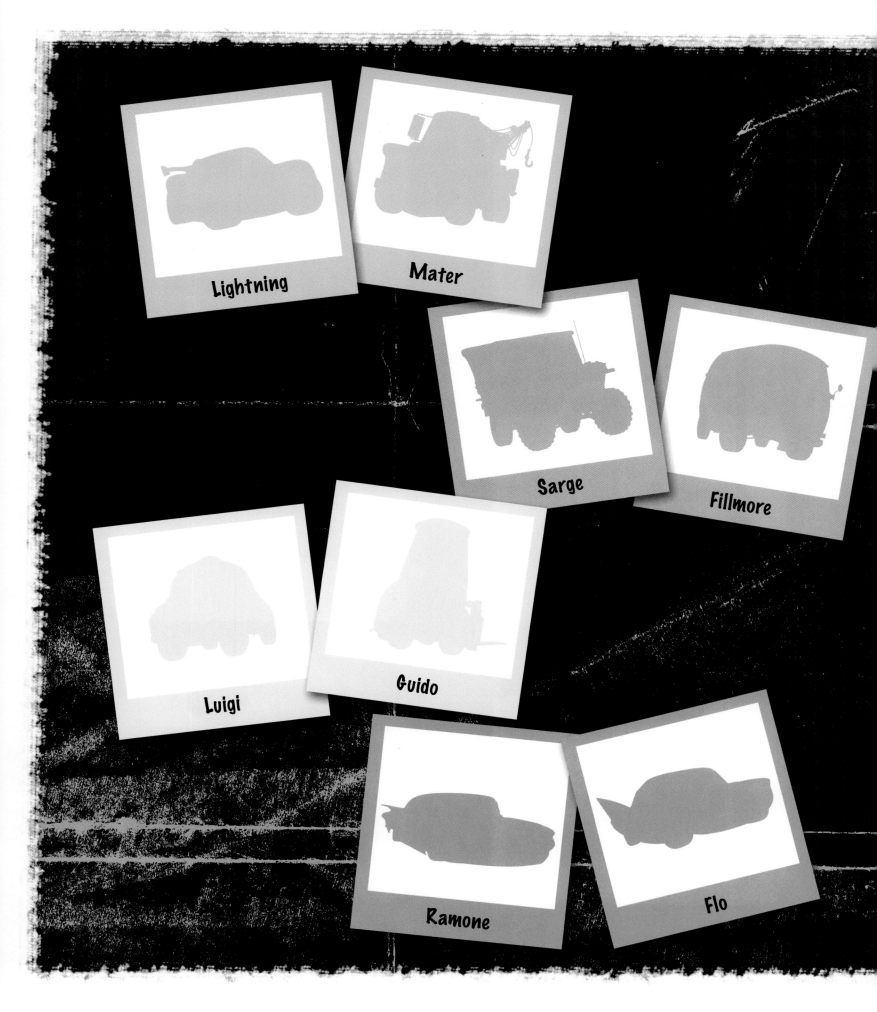

Lightning

Mater

Sarge

Fillmore

Luigi

Guido

Ramone

Flo

Holley

Finn

Alfa Duetto

Francesco

Grem

Acer

Kabuki Dancer

Sumo Wrestler

WELCOME TO TOKYO
Decorate this sleek Tokyo scene using your stickers.

THE GOOD, THE BAD, AND THE CREW

Use your stickers to put the vehicles in the correct groups.

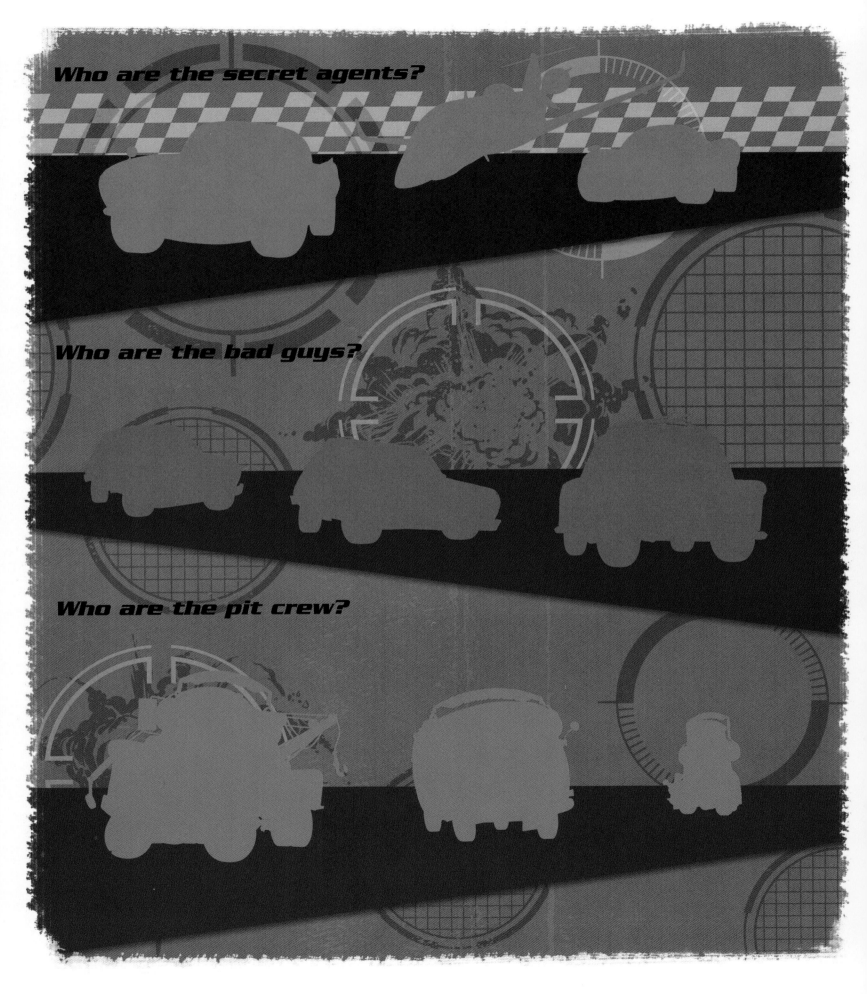

Who are the secret agents?

Who are the bad guys?

Who are the pit crew?

COUNTDOWN

Place your stickers over the shadows to get the right number in each box.

MATER PAYS A VISIT

Mater is off to meet Holley, but he sees some cars along the way. Who are they?

PIT STOP PATTERNS

Complete these patterns with the help of your stickers.

START YOUR ENGINES

Can you identify each of these cars? Place your stickers over the shadows.

Shu Todoroki

Jeff Gorvette

Lightning McQueen

Francesco Bernoulli

Rip Clutchgoneski

Miguel Camino

Max Schnell

Raoul ÇaRoule

SECRET AGENTS
Place each car above the right name using your stickers.

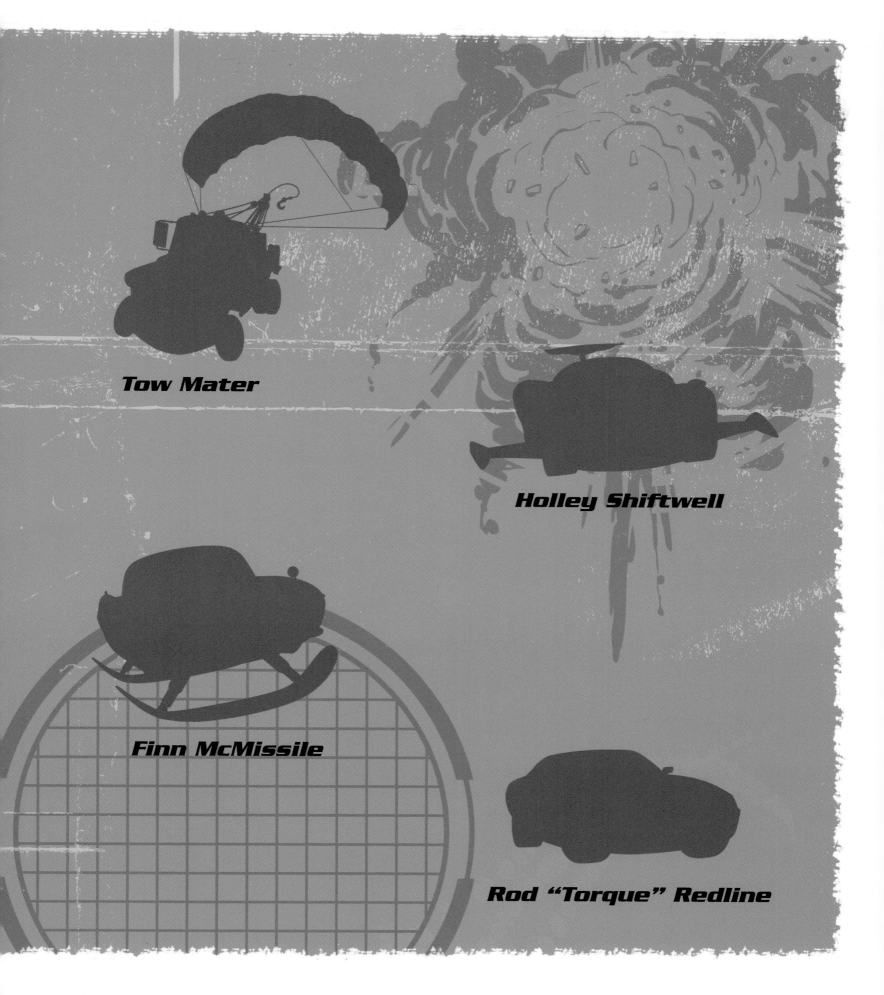

Tow Mater

Holley Shiftwell

Finn McMissile

Rod "Torque" Redline

IT'S A PIAZZA PARTY!

The cars visit Luigi and Guido's hometown! Decorate the scene using your stickers.

CAR OPPOSITES

The cars need your help to solve these opposites with your stickers.

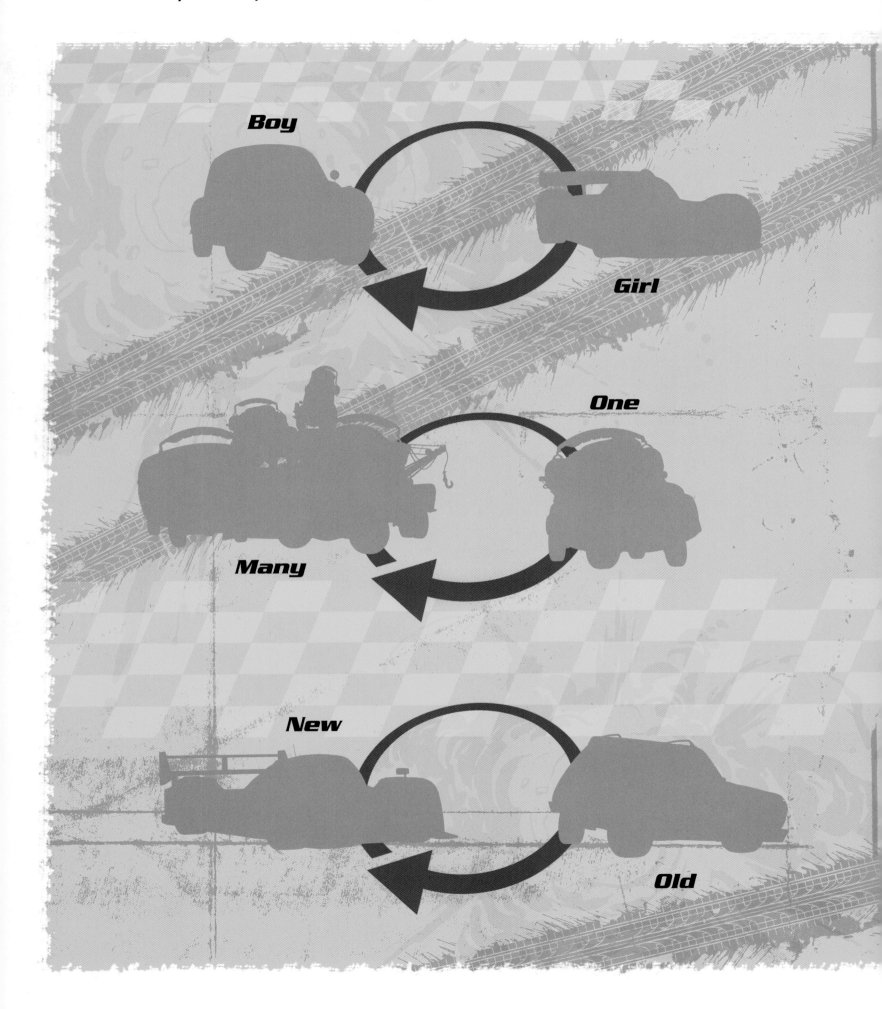

Boy

Girl

One

Many

New

Old

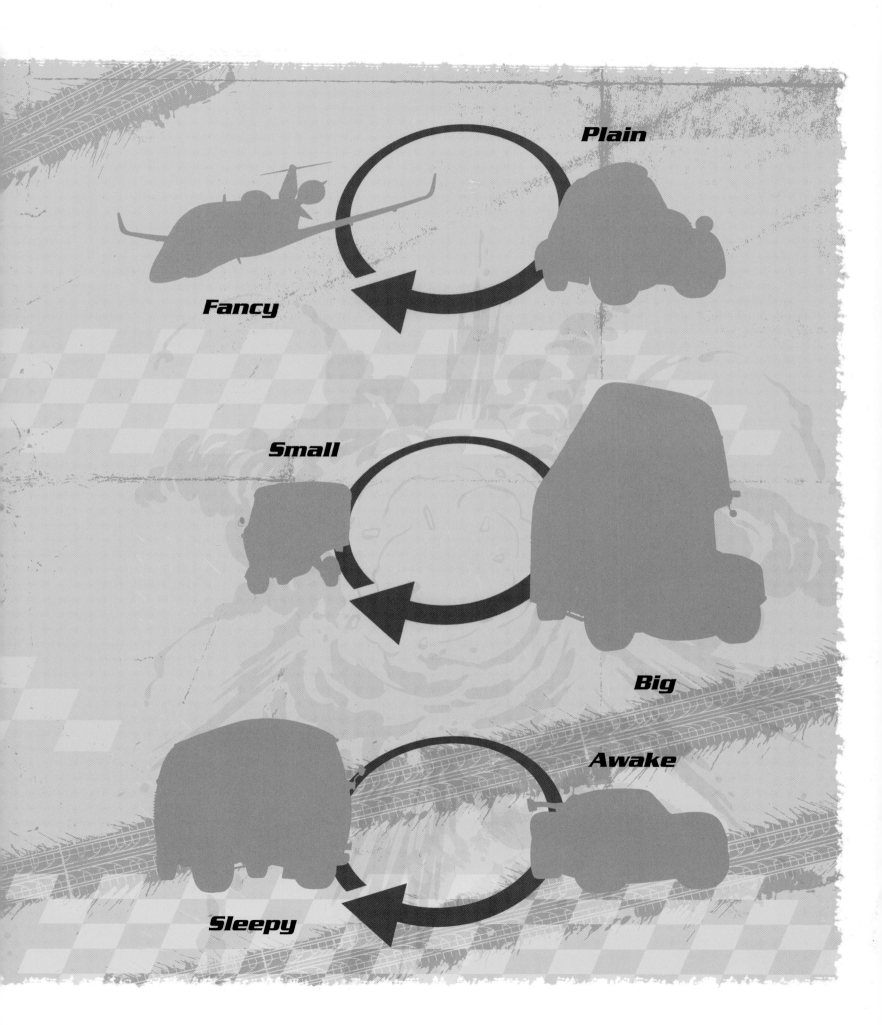

Plain

Fancy

Small

Big

Awake

Sleepy

MISSING PARTS

Place the parts over the right shadows to complete these characters.

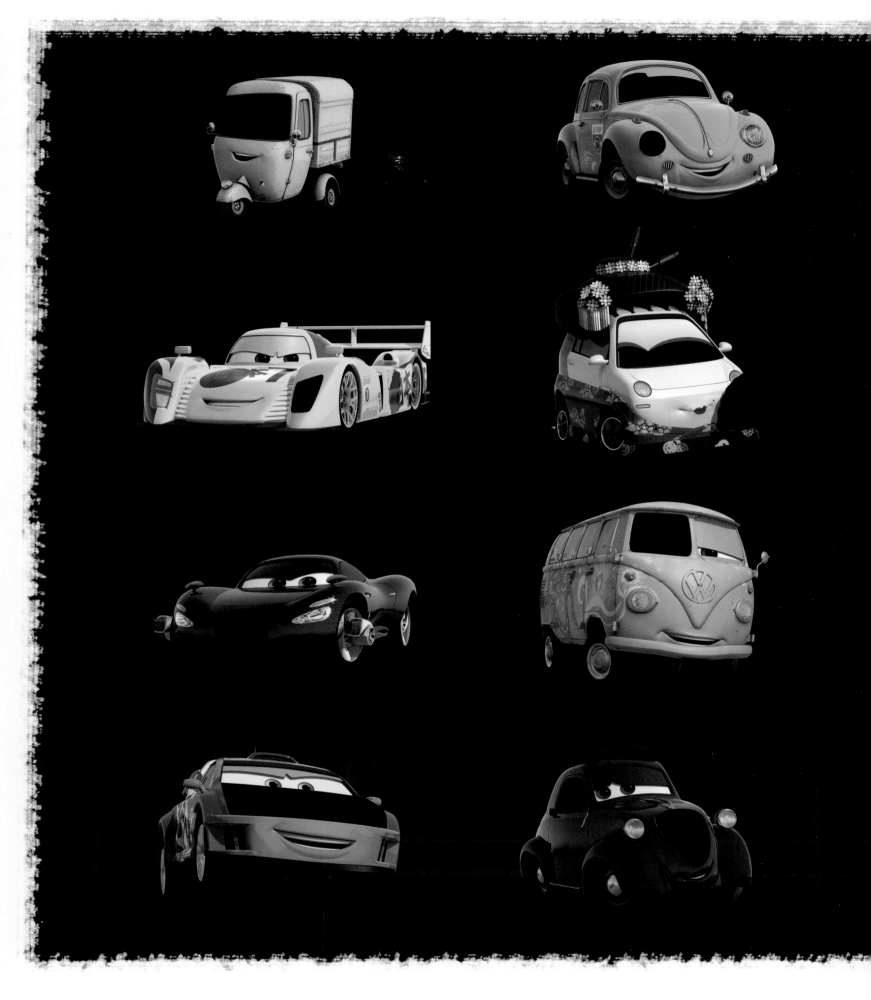

Behind the Scenes

Use your stickers to match the race cars to the right crew members.

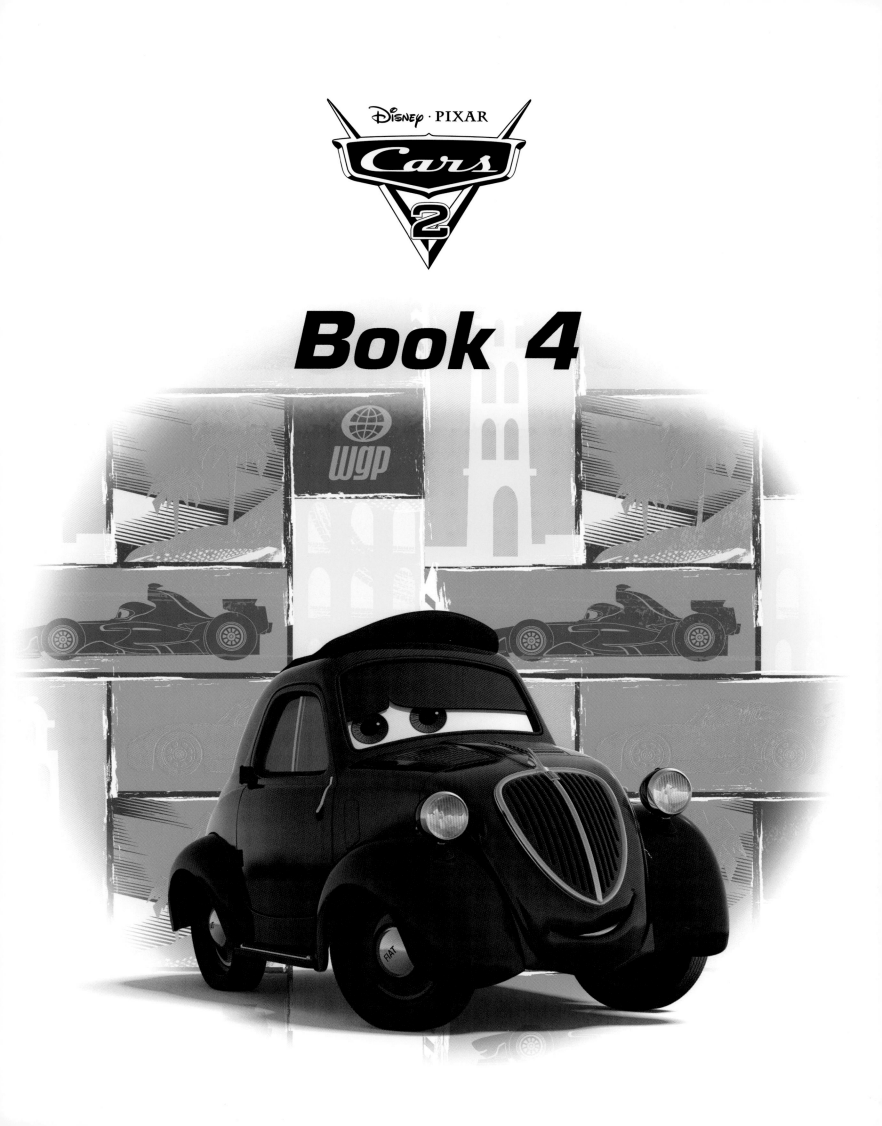

Car Colours

Place each car beside the matching colour using your stickers.

CAR CLOSE-UPS

Things look closer than they appear in the mirror! Match the cars to their close-ups.

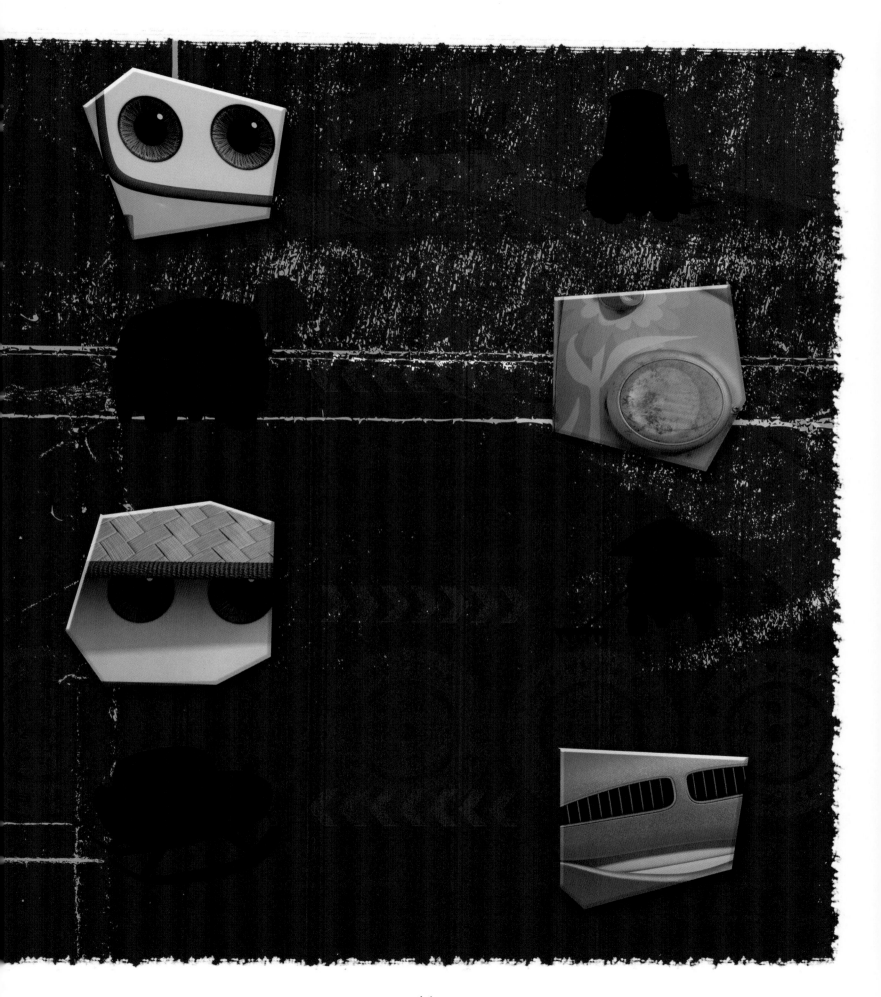

UNCLE TOPOLINO'S
Decorate Uncle Topolino's village using your stickers.

TIME TO ADD

Use your stickers to solve the addition problems below.

$$3 + 1 = 4$$

$$2 + 4 = 6$$

TIME TO SUBTRACT

Use your stickers to solve the subtraction problems below.

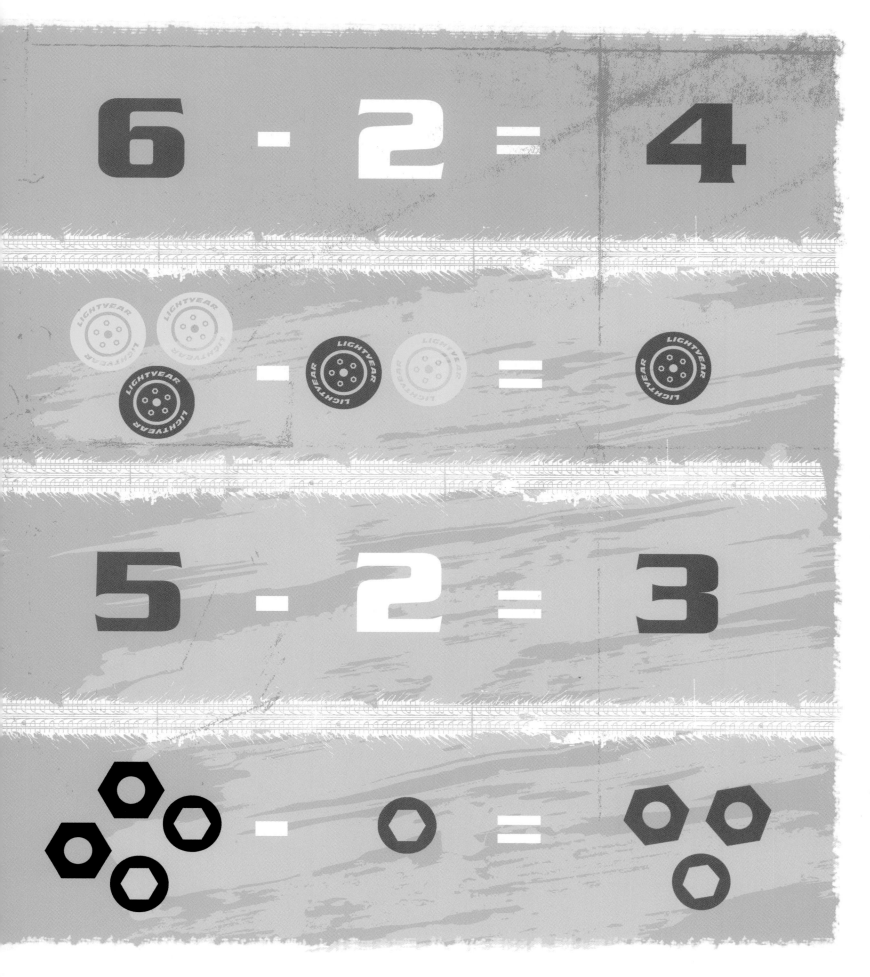

ROAD SHAPES

Use your stickers to help Mater and Finn identify the shapes.

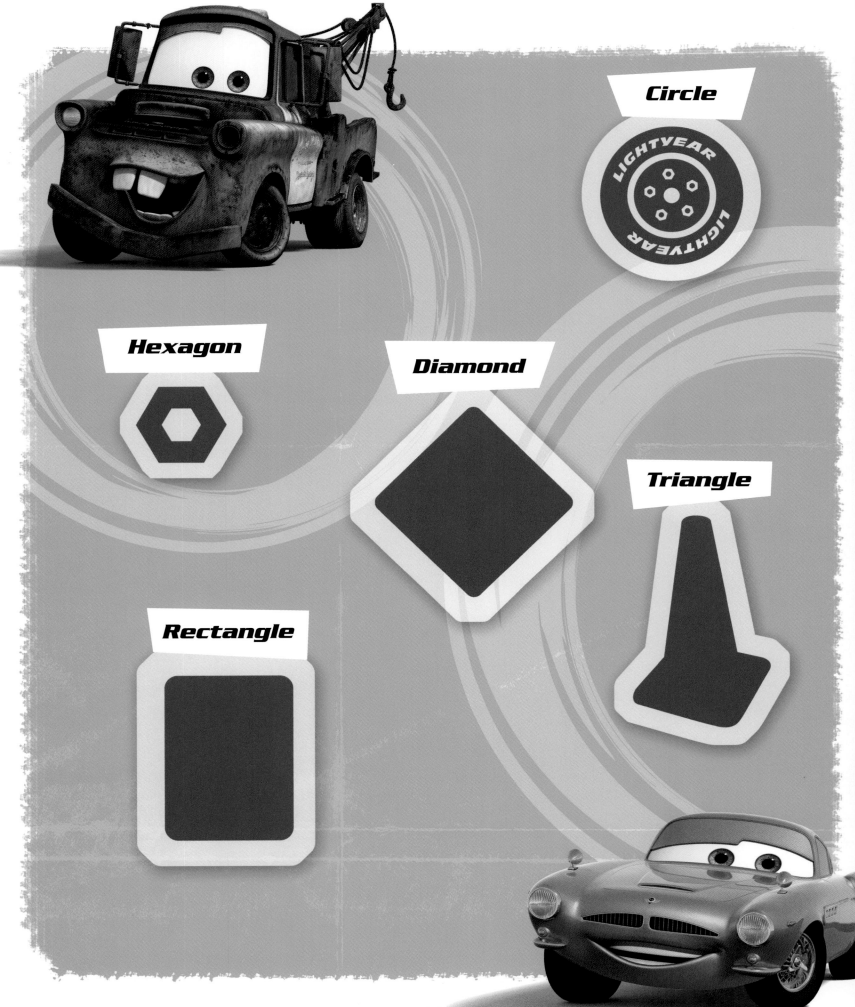

Circle

Hexagon

Diamond

Triangle

Rectangle

Cars of All Sizes

Sort your stickers from the biggest to the smallest.

TOKYO BY NIGHT
Make the bottom scene look like the top one with your stickers.

Book 5

MATER TO THE RESCUE

Lemons have a tendency to break down. Place your stickers over the shadows.

ALL EYES ON THE RACE
Cars everywhere are watching Lightning. Place your stickers over the shadows.

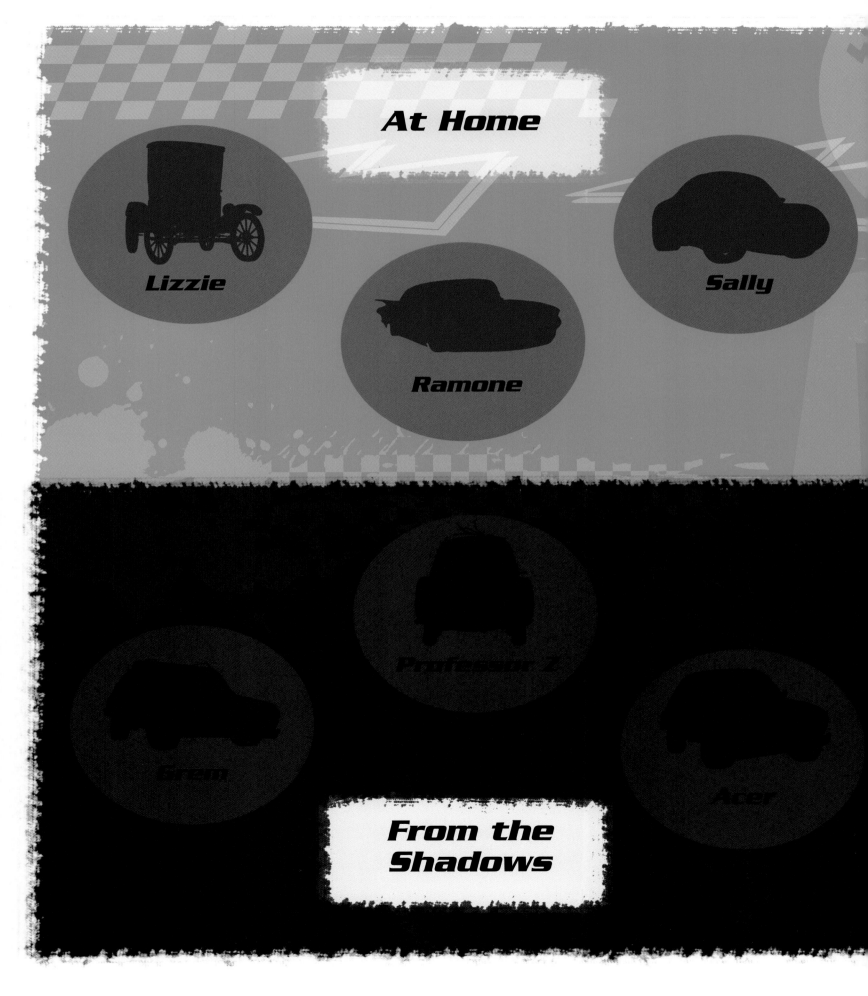

At Home

Lizzie

Ramone

Sally

Professor Z

Grem

Acer

From the
Shadows

On the Track

Shu

Francesco

Luigi

Holley

Mater

Finn

Undercover

SHU'S HOME COUNTRY

Shu Todoroki is proud of his heritage. Decorate the page with your stickers.

UNIQUE DESIGNS
Match the cars to their one-of-a-kind designs.

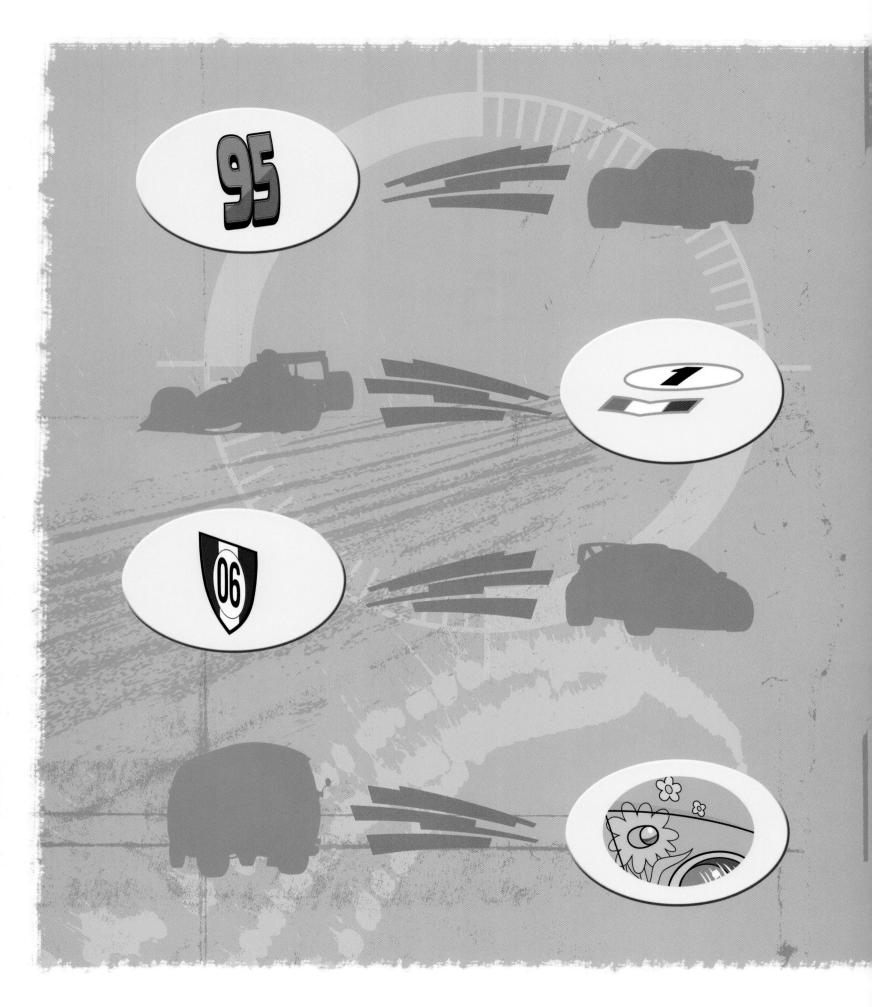

No Place Like Home

Place the stickers on the right shadows according to their home country.

Japan

England

Italy

USA

France

Japan

Germany

Italy

FILL IN THE BLANKS

Place your stickers over the shadows to make these vehicles complete.

SANTA RUOTINA

Uncle Topolino's village is beautiful! Make the bottom scene look like the top one.

MEET THE CARS

Meet the cars! Use the clues below to identify each character.

He's the Piston Cup champion.

He's Lightning McQueen's best friend.

He's Luigi's uncle.

He's a British secret agent.

He's a mad scientist.

He's a competitive Italian race car.

He's a popular French race car.

She's a secret agent-in-training.

ZOOMING IN

Can you identify each of these cars? Place your stickers next to their close-ups.

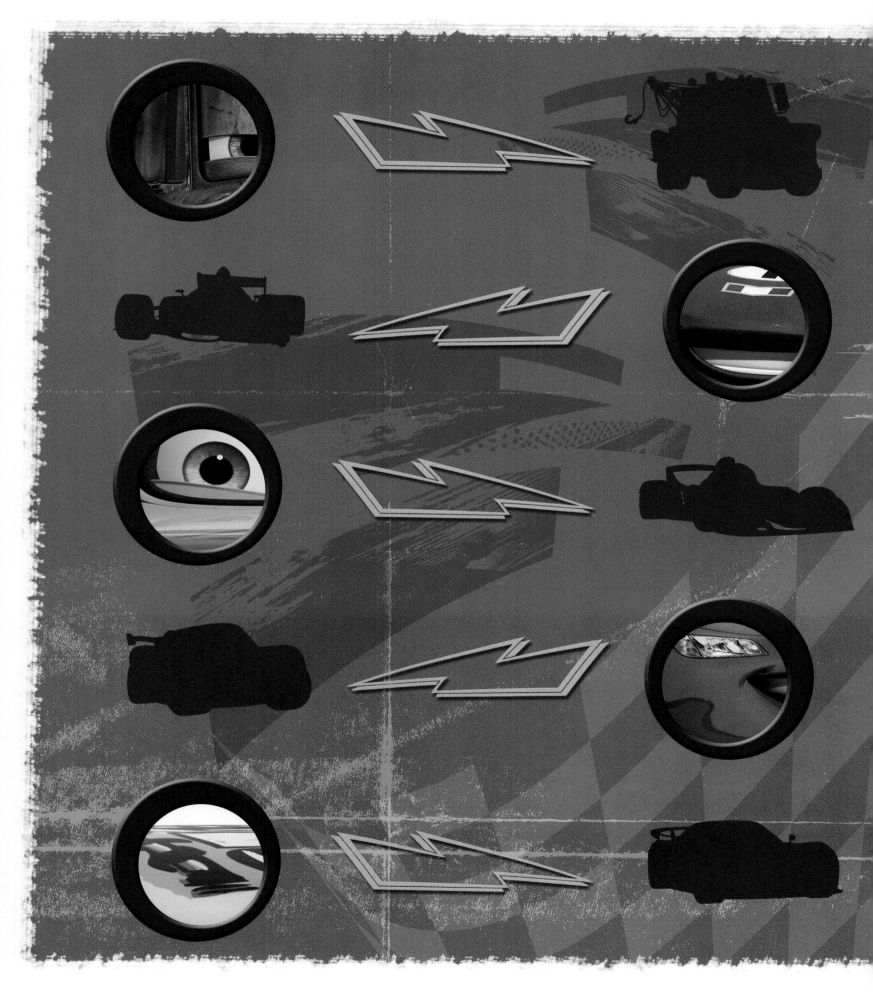

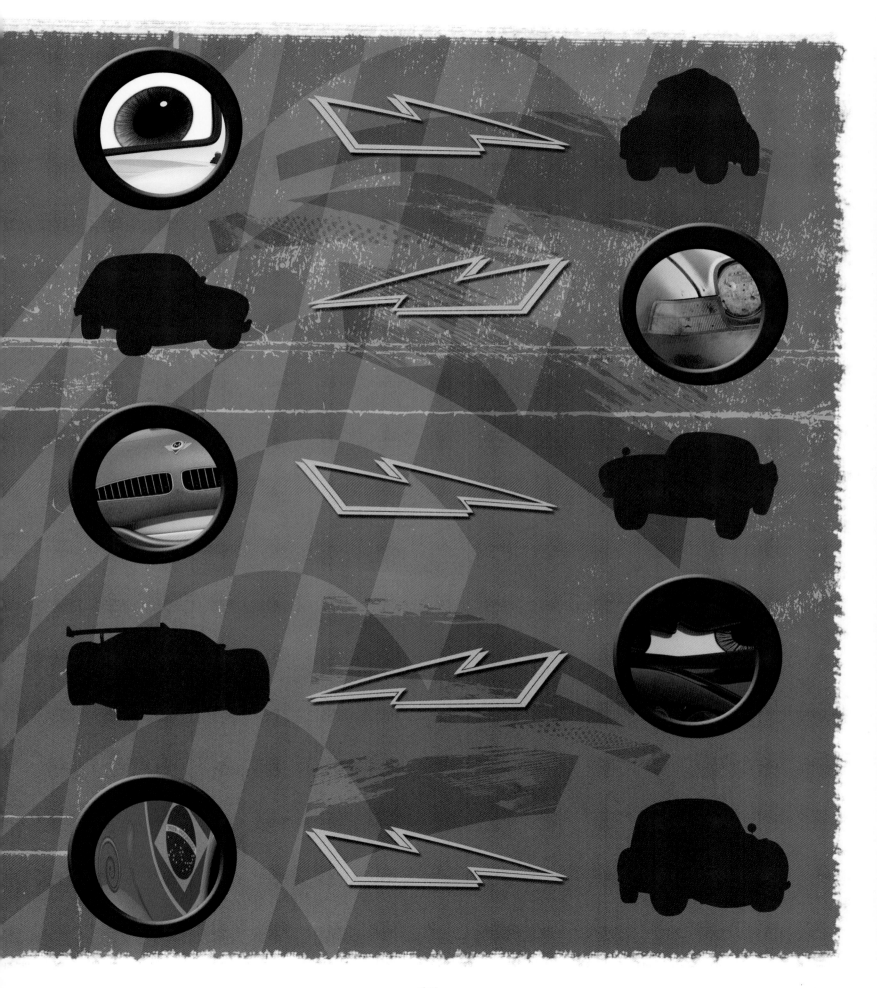

PORTO CORSA

The cars gear up for the big race in Italy! Decorate the scene with your stickers.

64 65

66 67

FOLLOW THE TRAIL

Follow the coloured trails to match each car to the right colour.

BODY WORK

Replace the missing car parts with the help of your stickers.

ALL IN ORDER

Use your stickers to complete the sequences below.